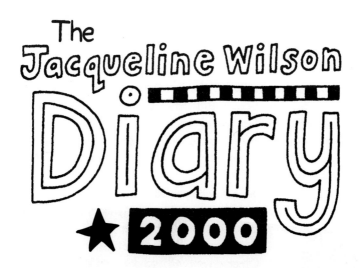

The Jacqueline Wilson Diary 2000

Illustrated by Nick Sharratt and Sue Heap

CORGI YEARLING BOOKS

Nick's Diary

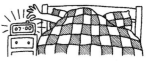

My alarm buzzes at seven each morning. I turn it off and nearly always roll over and go straight back to sleep. But I do have a strict rule that I must be sitting at my drawing board by nine at the latest and that can mean a mad dash, a gobbled breakfast and starting work in my nightshirt if I've had a longer than usual snooze. I work from home, in a room at the front of the house, so I can keep an eye on the goings-on in the street.

I love being an illustrator and I'm lucky enough to be busy all the time. Sometimes I go to schools or book events or I have meetings in London but most days I'm in my studio.

I have lots of projects on the go at the same time, and I hardly ever spend the whole day working on just one book. I use the mornings for 'thinking' work: coming up with ideas and doing rough sketches. If my brain's not functioning properly I run round to the baker's for a sticky bun and that always does the trick. I work till one and then I have an hour off for lunch and I'll read a newspaper or magazine while I eat.

I'm most likely to spend the afternoon on final artwork. I use charcoal a lot, and watercolour inks and I draw my black and white illustrations with a technical pen. I'll have the radio on or maybe a C.D. Seventies disco is good working music, so are soundtracks from James Bond films.

I work until seven, then I force myself to go for a swim: I need the exercise after sitting down all day. And I might see friends. With any luck it will be their turn to provide the food. I love to eat but when it comes to cooking I'm completely useless!

All About Me

My name is ....

My address is ....

....

....

I am .... years .... months old

My birthday is on ....

I am .... m .... cm tall

I weigh .... kg

My eyes are ....

My skin is ....

My hair is ....

Here is a picture of Tracy Beaker.
You can put your picture
under Tracy's.

Here is a photo of me

My Family

Dolphin lives with her sister and her mum. Elsa lives with her mum, her mum's boyfriend and her little half-sister and half-brother. Mandy lives with her mummy and daddy but doesn't have any brothers or sisters. Who do you live with?

I live with: ...my mum, my dad... ....and my younger brother.......
....
....

Jessie Me Rose Frank Mother and Ada-May

We live in a : ....
....
....
....

Oxford Terrace. Wow!

We have these pets: ....
....
....

School

My school is called: ....
....

My favourite subject is : ....
....

My worst subject is: ....
....

At playtime I: ....
....

My favourite teacher is: ....
....

Miss Beckworth

I like sitting next to: ....
....

We have to wear: ....
....
....

Friends

These are my friends:

Name:	Known since:
....	....
....	....
....	....
....	....
....	....
....	....
....	....
....	....
....	....
....	....
....	....
....	....
....	....

Birthdays

These are the birthdays I want to remember:

Name:	Date:

Things I Like And Don't Like

I like eating: ....Chocolate (mmmm!)....
....Chicken and bacon...
pizza (yum!)

I hate eating: ....bannana yuck!..
..my most hated of all foods.

My hobbies are:
....Clarenet., art (any shape....
....or form)
....

I don't like doing: ....
....

I like it when the weather is:
....

I don't like the weather when: ....
....

I like feeling: ....

I don't like feeling: ....

My favourite book is:

....

I didn't enjoy reading:

....

My favourite TV programme is:

....

I don't like watching: ....

The colour I like most is: ....

My least favourite colour is: ....

My favourite animal is: ....

....

The animals I don't like are:

....

....

Have You Read All These Books By Jacqueline Wilson?

The Dinosaur's Packed Lunch
I thought this book was ....

The Monster Story-teller
I thought this book was ....

The Illustrated Mum
I thought this book was .... MICKY

The Lottie Project
I thought this book was ....

Cliffhanger
I thought this book was ....

Buried Alive!
I thought this book was ....

The Story of Tracy Beaker
I thought this book was ....

The Suitcase Kid
I thought this book was ....

The Mum-Minder
I thought this book was ....

✓

The Bed and Breakfast Star
I thought this book was ....

✓

Double Act
I thought this book was ....

✓

Bad Girls
I thought this book was ....

Glubbslyme
I thought this book was ....

✓

Girls in Love
I thought this book was ....

✓

Girls Under Pressure
I thought this book was ....

Girls out Late
I thought this book was

....

Address Book

Name	Address	Phone No.

POST CARD

Dear Mum and Dad
I am at the Adventure Centre.
Well You know that. You took
me here. I have only been here half an
hour. I am not enjoying it so
far. Not one bit.
With love from
Tom
xxxxxxxx to Mum
x to Dad

Mr and Mrs R. Parsons,
10 Rainbow Street,
Didcot,
Oxon

Name	Address	Phone No.

Name	Address	Phone No.

POST CARD

Dear Mom and Dad
Us Tigers all got into Mega-Trouble
last night. But it was good fun all
the same. And then Kelly gave me a
Kit Kat before we went to bed. I
shared it with Biscuits. I had the
Kit and he had the Kat. Biscuits is
my friend. And Kelly. Even though
she's a girl.   With love from
                    Tim xxxxx
P.S. we're doing the Crazy Bucket race
today. Weird! How can you race
buckets????

Mr and Mrs R. Parsons,
10 Rainbow Street,
Didcot,
Oxon

Name	Address	Phone No.

Name	Address	Phone No.

Name	Address	Phone No.
....	....	....
....	....	....
....	....	....
....	....	....
....	....	....
....	....	....
....	....	....
....	....	....
....	....	....
....	....	....
....	....	....
....	....	....
....	....	....
....	....	....
....	....	....
....	....	....

POST CARD

Dear Biscuits-Boy
I wish we were still having
Adventures! My dad is ever
so chuffed we won. My mum is
just glad I'm back safe. She says
to ask your mum if you can come
and stay. Kelly might be coming
too. Has she written to you? She's
written to me twice already!
How many biscuits have you
consumed since I saw you?
Is it A) 10   B) 100   C) 1000 ???
Your pal
Super-Tim

Mr 'Biscuits' Baker,
39 Marlow Road,
Market Harborough,
Leicestershire

My Plans For The Year 2000

This year I aim to ..... Keep a diary for the year 200. Well, hopefully I can hang on longer than January this time! Wish me luck.

This year I would like to (Dream to.) I Dream to be noticed by an agent for some-thing eg: Looks = modeling, cover girl, acting = & perhaps to perform in something open to the public

DOWNING ST.
10

This year I will not ....
....
....
....
....
....
....
....
....
....
....

This year I really hope ..Me...and...~~he~~....
...richard...(who...I...secretly
...fancy...)...will...get...together.
...if...not...I...am...going...to
...write...my...feelings...down...in
...a...letter...and...post...it
...to...him.
....
....
....
....
....
....

Dec / January

TRACY'S DIARY

New Year Resolutions!

Elaine the Pain (my boring old social worker) says I should try to Calm Down. She says I am too fizzy, like a bottle of lemonade all shaken up. Great. I can't wait for someone to unscrew my head and then I shall EXPLODE. All over Justine Littlewood. I can't stick her. So...my first Resolution will be:

1. Make Justine Littlewood look a total berk.
2. Stay friends with Louise.
3. Don't make friends with Weedy Peter.
4. Get myself a foster mum unless I...
5. SEE MY REAL MUM.

(Read about Tracy in THE STORY OF TRACY BEAKER)

Monday 27

Tuesday 28

Wednesday 29

Thursday 30

Friday 31

Saturday 1 / Sunday 2

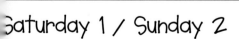

January

THIS ROOM BELONGS TO
TRACY BEAKER
STRICTLY PRIVATE
KEEP OUT ON PAIN OF DEATH.
AND IT WILL BE A VERY PAINFUL
DEATH TOO.

Monday 3

Tuesday 4

Wednesday 5

My Birthday

Thursday 6   Back to school (groan)

Friday 7

Saturday 8

Sunday 9

2000

January

Buy some decent clothes.

Monday 10

Tuesday 11

Wednesday 12

Thursday 13

Friday 14

Saturday 15

Sunday 16

2000

January

Monday 17

Tuesday 18

Wednesday 19

Thursday 20

Friday 21

Saturday 22

Sunday 23

January

Cross

"Just words. Cross words!"

Monday 24

Tuesday 25

Wednesday 26

Thursday 27

Friday 28

Saturday 29

Sunday 30

2000

Jan / February

Mum's got flu so I had to help look after all the babies today. It was hard work. They were very-very-very-very naughty.

Gemma got Mum's make-up bag and played Pretty Ladies. Vincent nicked the lipstick and drew a red picture on the white wall. Baby Clive drank his bottle much too quickly and then slurped it all down my best T-shirt. And my own little sister Sara pulled the head off my Barbie doll and threw it down the toilet.

I am sick of babies. I am not going to be a child-minder like my mum when I grow up.

(Read about Sadie in THE MUM-MINDER)

Monday 31

Tuesday 1

Wednesday 2

Thursday 3

Friday 4

Saturday 5 / Sunday 6

2000

February

For two ultra-chatty people we suddenly seemed lost for words.

Monday 7

Tuesday 8

Wednesday 9

Thursday 10

Friday 11

Saturday 12

Sunday 13

2000

February

The mere thought of Jamie Edwards acting lovey-dovey was enough to crease me up.

Monday 14

Tuesday 15

Wednesday 16

Thursday 17

Friday 18

Saturday 19

I wish I really had a boyfriend.

Sunday 20

2000

February

Jamie kept walking closer and closer to me, so that his schoolbag banged his shins several times. I turned to tell him off – and he kissed me on the cheek!

Monday 21

Tuesday 22

Wednesday 23

Thursday 24

Friday 25

Saturday 26

Sunday 27

2000

Feb/March

RUBY AND GARNET'S DIARY
We are identical twins. I'm Ruby. I'm the boss.
I'm Garnet. I do what Ruby says. Sometimes!

    It was an ace day today. Garnet and I did our Double Act all the time. We went marching down to breakfast in step and ate our corn-flakes spoon by spoon in perfect timing. Rose thought it so spooky she spilt her coffee.

    Poor Rose was wearing her new red shirt.

    Yeah, it was ruined. Great! Red's our colour. Rubies and garnets are red jewels. They look alike. Like us. Though rubies are actually much more valuable. Ha!

(Read about Ruby and Garnet in DOUBLE ACT)

Monday 28

Tuesday 29

Wednesday 1

Thursday 2

Friday 3

Saturday 4 / Sunday 5

March

He said her name specially, as if a real little star sparkled on his lips.

Monday 6

Tuesday 7

Wednesday 8

Thursday 9

Friday 10

Saturday 11

Sunday 12

2000

March

*Kelly's the sort of girl who doesn't
care about anything.*

Monday 13

Tuesday 14

Wednesday 15

Thursday 16

Friday 17

Saturday 18

Sunday 19

2000

March

*'I don't care,' said Dinah,
sucking her thumb.*

Monday 20

Tuesday 21

Wednesday 22

Thursday 23

Friday 24

Saturday 25

Sunday 26

2000

March/April

REBECCA'S DIARY

My magical toad Glubbslyme made me take him to school today. I hid him in my lunch box. He ate all my lunch. He didn't even enjoy it.

'I do not care for cheese rolls and salt and vinegar crisps, Rebecca. It is time to educate your palate. A dainty slug sandwich and a little worm pâté would be far more sophisticated.'

Glubbslyme isn't always sophisticated himself. When I took him for a quick bath in the washbasin in the girls' cloakrooms he wanted to go for a paddle in the toilet!

(Read about Rebecca in GLUBBSLYME)

Monday 27

Tuesday 28

Wednesday 29

Thursday 30

Friday 31

Saturday 1 / Sunday 2

April

'I want it to be a picture on me,'
said Marigold.

Monday 3

Tuesday 4

Wednesday 5

Thursday 6

Friday 7

Saturday 8

Sunday 9

2000

April

'Come out here, Natalie. So you like telling stories?'

Monday 10

Tuesday 11

Wednesday 12

Thursday 13

Friday 14

Saturday 15

Sunday 16

2000

 # April

I've done a bit of stamping and screaming in my time.

Monday 17

Tuesday 18

Wednesday 19

Thursday 20

Friday 21

Saturday 22

Sunday 23

April

Monday 24

Tuesday 25

Wednesday 26

Thursday 27

Friday 28

Saturday 29

Sunday 30

*Sunday is meant to be a day of rest. Well,
ha ha. There's no rest as far as I'm concerned.*

2000

May

DOLPHIN'S DIARY

I cant rite much becos I am ~~dislecksick~~ ~~dyslegsyc~~
Im not good with words.

But Im grate at pickurs. So is Marigold my
mum. She is lik a walking pickur book. I love her
so much even tho she is sumtimes scary.

(Read about Dolphin in
THE ILLUSTRATED MUM)

Monday 1

Tuesday 2

Wednesday 3

Thursday 4

Friday 5

Saturday 6 / Sunday 7

2000

May

Monday 8

Tuesday 9

Wednesday 10

Thursday 11

Friday 12

Saturday 13

Sunday 14

2000

May

Mum fixed me a special sick-bed tea...

Monday 15

Tuesday 16

Wednesday 17

Thursday 18

Friday 19

Saturday 20

Sunday 21

2000

May

I wish I could get to sleep.
I'll try counting sheep...

Monday 22

Tuesday 23

Wednesday 24

Thursday 25

Friday 26

Saturday 27

Sunday 28

2000

May / June

MANDY'S DIARY

I can't wait till the end of term. I hate school now. Kim and Melanie and Sarah are being so hateful to me. They did silly bunny hops down the corridor when they saw me coming. It's because Mum knitted these awful baby bunnies on my cardigan. Then they all twitched their noses like rabbits and squealed with laughter.

Still I don't care so much now because I've got my best ever friend Tanya and we're going to spend ALL the summer holidays together.

(Read about Mandy in BAD GIRLS)

Monday 29

Tuesday 30

Wednesday 31

Thursday 1

Friday 2

Saturday 3 / Sunday 4

June

She seemed too lightly linked together, almost as fragile as the daisy chain round her ankle.

Monday 5

Tuesday 6

Wednesday 7

Thursday 8

Friday 9

Saturday 10

Sunday 11

2000

June

Monday 12

Tuesday 13

Wednesday 14

Thursday 15

Friday 16

Saturday 17

Sunday 18

June

Monday 19

Tuesday 20

Wednesday 21

Thursday 22

Friday 23

Saturday 24

Sunday 25

2000

June / July

TIM'S DIARY

I don't like it at the Adventure Centre. Not one bit. I can't stand Giles. He keeps teasing me. And he shouted when I was useless at games.

Biscuits didn't shout. Biscuits is my new friend. He shared his tin of golden syrup with me. My fingers are still a bit sticky. I shall have to be careful not to stick these pages together. But maybe this is the very last day I shall write this diary. Tomorrow I have to go ABSEILING. I doubt I shall survive.

(Read about Tim in CLIFFHANGER)

Monday 26

Tuesday 27

Wednesday 28

Thursday 29

Friday 30

Saturday 1 / Sunday 2

2000

July

Monday 3

Tuesday 4

Wednesday 5

Thursday 6

Friday 7

Saturday 8

Sunday 9

2000

July

She scooped her troll out of the little pool and was holding her at arm's length.

Monday 10

Tuesday 11

Wednesday 12

Thursday 13

Friday 14

Saturday 15

Sunday 16

2000

July

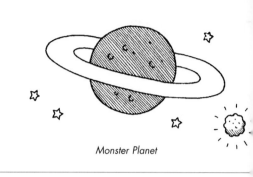

Monster Planet

Monday 17

Tuesday 18

Wednesday 19

Thursday 20

Friday 21

Saturday 22

Sunday 23

2000

July

*We've had to leave our school. It was awful
saying goodbye.*

Monday 24

Tuesday 25

Wednesday 26

Thursday 27

Friday 28

My first ice-cream! This time my lips turned blue but I licked them warm again.

Saturday 29

Sunday 30

2000

July / August

BISCUITS'S DIARY

I had egg and bacon for breakfast and four sausages. (Tim doesn't like sausages so I had his. He is crackers.) I also had five slices of toast and six spoonfuls of sugar in my tea. I was starving all morning. I just had one ice-cream to keep me going (plus my secret supply of chocolate biscuits).

We had a picnic on the beach for lunch. I had ten sandwiches and three sausage rolls and a giant bag of crisps and two apples and a Kit Kat and a can of Coke.

It was fish and chips for tea, yum yum, and then we had pizza for supper and I had every single topping on mine, MEGA yum!

(Read about Biscuits in BURIED ALIVE!)

Monday 31

Tuesday 1

Wednesday 2

Thursday 3

Friday 4

Biscuits ate my tea as well as his own.

Saturday 5 / Sunday 6

August

I laboured long and hard making a sandcastle for Robin – I was beginning to think I'd maybe done enough hard labour and that it was time I was let off for good behaviour.

Monday 7

Tuesday 8

Wednesday 9

Thursday 10

Friday 11

Saturday 12

Sunday 13

2000

August

*'Let's build a motte and bailey castle, eh,
Biscuits?' I said.
'You what?' said Biscuits. 'Bot and naily?'*

Monday 14

Tuesday 15

Wednesday 16

Thursday 17

Friday 18

Saturday 19

Sunday 20

2000

August

I'd been looking forward to my holiday for ages and ages.

Monday 21

Tuesday 22

Wednesday 23

'Hey, I'm glad this isn't an adventure holiday like last time.'
'You can say that again!'
'I'm glad this isn't an adventure holiday like last time.'

Thursday 24

Friday 25

Saturday 26

Sunday 27

2000

Aug/September

ELLIE'S DIARY

I saw that blond boy on the way to school. He smiled at me again. He is so wonderful. He looked particularly great today in a white T-shirt.

If only I didn't have to wear my stupid school uniform. If only I wasn't short and fat, with frizzy hair and glasses. I wish I looked like Nadine. I wish I looked like Magda. I wish I looked like anyone else but me!

(Read about Ellie in GIRLS IN LOVE, GIRLS UNDER PRESSURE and GIRLS OUT LATE)

Monday 28

Tuesday 29

Wednesday 30

Thursday 31

Friday 1

Saturday 2 / Sunday 3

September

Monday 4

Tuesday 5

Wednesday 6

Thursday 7

Friday 8

Saturday 9

Sunday 10

2000

September

*Guess what happened that first day of term.
We got this new teacher.*

Miss Beckworth

Monday 11

Tuesday 12

Wednesday 13

Thursday 14

Friday 15

Saturday 16

Sunday 17

2000

September

Garnet got dressed in her strange new uniform.

Monday 18

Tuesday 19

Wednesday 20

Thursday 21

Friday 22

Saturday 23

Sunday 24

2000

Sept/October

CHARLIE'S DIARY

I went out Trick or Treating at Halloween with Angela and Lisa. I dressed up as a vampire. I looked very convincing, with dribbles of blood down my chin (Jo's scarlet lipstick). I threatened to bite people unless they gave us lots of treats. We ended up with heaps. We shared them out. I bagged all the Smarties for my cake decorating (plus I like them best).

I wonder if they went Trick or Treating in Victorian times? I don't think poor Lottie had many treats at all.

(Read about Charlie in
THE LOTTIE PROJECT)

Lisa   Me   Angela

Monday 25

Tuesday 26

Wednesday 27

Thursday 28

Friday 29

Saturday 30 / Sunday 1

2000

October

The iguanodon reached down and picked Dinah up.

Monday 2

Tuesday 3

Wednesday 4

Thursday 5

Friday 6

Saturday 7

Sunday 8

2000

October

You've got to have this great big
s-s-s-m-m-m-i-i-i-l-l-l-e-e-e-.

Monday 9

Tuesday 10

Wednesday 11

Thursday 12

Friday 13

Saturday 14

Sunday 15

2000

October

'You can try them on if you want.'

Monday 16

Tuesday 17

Wednesday 18

Thursday 19

Friday 20

Saturday 21

Sunday 22

2000

October

Monday 23

Tuesday 24

Wednesday 25

Thursday 26

Friday 27

Saturday 28

Sunday 29

Oct/November

ELSA'S DIARY

November. I don't like words with NO in them. People are always saying NO to me.

Mum says, "No Elsa, I feel too fed up to go round to the shops."

Mack the Smack says, "No Elsa, you little whatsit, you can't have any fireworks, think I'm made of money?"

Pippa says, "No Elsa, I don't want to go to the toilet" – and then she wets herself.

Hank says, "NO NO NO" – but he says that to everyone.

Hey, my mate Funny-Face says he knows a way to get into the park free to see the special Firework Display and do I want to come?

YES YES YES!

(Read about Elsa in THE BED AND BREAKFAST STAR)

Monday 30

Tuesday 31

Wednesday 1

Thursday 2

Friday 3

Saturday 4 / Sunday 5

2000

November

There was a phone call for me at tea time.

Monday 6

Tuesday 7

Wednesday 8

Thursday 9

Friday 10

Saturday 11

Sunday 12

2
0
0
0

November

*'Dolphin? Ooh, I say. I've never met a Dolphin before.
What a lovely name.'*

Monday 13

Tuesday 14

Wednesday 15

Thursday 16

Friday 17

Saturday 18

Sunday 19

2000

November

I was delighted at breakfast to see that Justine has a swollen nose and a sticking plaster.

Monday 20

Tuesday 21

Wednesday 22

Thursday 23

Friday 24

Saturday 25

Sunday 26

2000

Nov/December

ANDY'S DIARY

The best thing about having two families is having two lots of
Christmas presents! This year will be extra special because it's my
half-sister Zoe's first Christmas. She is very nearly one. She looks
like me. I even brush her hair into this funny little fringe like mine.

She loves the fairy lights on the Christmas tree. I hold her up so
she can see them properly. Dad said I should make a little fairy outfit
for my special lucky mascot rabbit Radish so she can go on top of the
Christmas tree.

Mum said I should make Radish a little red suit and stick cotton
wool on her chin and turn her into Santa Paws. I've knitted three
special Christmas stockings to hang up this year. A big one for me.
A little one for Zoe. And a weeny teeny one for Radish.

(Read about Andy in THE SUITCASE KID)

Monday 27

Tuesday 28

Wednesday 29

Thursday 30

Friday 1

Saturday 2 / Sunday 3

December

'He tickles,' said Tanya.

Monday 4

Tuesday 5

Wednesday 6

Thursday 7

Friday 8

Saturday 9

Sunday 10

2000

December

'I'm going to be so busy busy busy making cakes in the Christmas holidays.'

Monday 11

Tuesday 12

Wednesday 13

Thursday 14

Friday 15

Saturday 16

Sunday 17

2000

December

Monday 18

Tuesday 19

Wednesday 20

Thursday 21

Friday 22

*'So why can't we all come to you for
Christmas, Gran, and then we can
have Christmas dinner, with
cranberry sauce and little chipolatas,
yummy yummy,' said Ruby.*

Saturday 23

Sunday 24

December

is for Xmas

Monday 25

"I'm going to get to eat the angel on Christmas Day - because I'm currently so angelic!"

Tuesday 26

Wednesday 27

Thursday 28

Friday 29

Saturday 30

Sunday 31

2000

THE JACQUELINE WILSON DIARY 2000
A CORGI YEARLING BOOK: 0 440 864232

First publication in Great Britain

PRINTING HISTORY
Corgi Yearling edition published 1999

Corgi Yearling Books are published by
Transworld Publishers Ltd,
61-63 Uxbridge Road, Ealing, London W5 5SA,
in Australia by Transworld Publishers,
c/o Random House Australia Pty Ltd, 20 Alfred Street,
Milsons Point, NSW 2061, Australia,
in New Zealand by Transworld Publishers,
c/o Random House New Zealand, 18 Poland Road, Glenfield,
Auckland, New Zealand,
and in South Africa by Transworld Publishers,
c/o Random House (Pty) Ltd, Endulini, 5a Jubilee Road,
Parktown 2193, South Africa

Made and printed in Great Britain by
Ebenezer Baylis and Son (Printers) Ltd, Worcester, Worcs

Jacqueline's Diary

I crawl out of bed at seven o'clock every morning and walk down the road to the swimming baths. I swim 50 lengths, making up all sorts of things in my head. Sometimes I think sensible thoughts about the stories I write. Other times I daydream daft things, pretending I'm a shipwreck survivor, a mermaid — even a dolphin! My hair is so short that it's dry by the time I get home.

I have my breakfast and open all my post. I get lots of letters from children. My lucky mascot rabbit Radish often gets her own letters too!

Then I start writing. Sometimes I write at home. Other days I visit schools and libraries so I write on the train. I write in longhand in fat spiral notebooks. Sometimes I use a special colour pen for a certain sort of story. I choose black for scary scenes and draw big black spiders, snakes and skulls at the corners of the page. If I write a love scene I swap to pink and doodle hearts all round the edge.

I like days when I talk to children. Radish generally comes too and demonstrates her Bunny-Bungee-Jumping trick.

In the evening I always telephone my daughter Emma and we talk for ages. Some nights I see my friends. I take part in a quiz once a week — and I also go line dancing!

I go to bed with a book. I never run out of reading material — I have more than 10,000 books crammed into my tiny house. The very last thing I do each night is...write my diary.

very short hair

lots of jewellery

black cloth but they'll all blotchy I ink them

more jewellery

pointy boot